This book belongs to

....

Super Dad and Other Stories

How this collection works

This *Biff, Chip and Kipper* collection is one of a series of four books at **Read with Oxford Stage 2**. It is divided into two distinct halves.

The first half focuses on phonics, with two stories written in line with the phonics your child will have learned at school: *Such a Fuss* and *The Moon Jet*. The second half contains two stories that use everyday language: *Super Dad* and *The Spaceship*. These stories help to broaden your child's wider reading experience. There are also fun activities to enjoy throughout the book.

How to use this book

Find a time to read with your child when they are not too tired and are happy to concentrate for about ten to fifteen minutes. Reading at this stage should be a shared and enjoyable experience. It is best to choose just one story for each session.

There are tips for each part of the book to help you make the most of the stories and activities. The tips for reading on pages 6 and 28 show you how to introduce your child to the phonics stories.

The tips for reading on pages 50 and 72 explain how you can best approach reading the stories that use a wider vocabulary. At the end of each of the four stories you will find four 'Talk about the story' questions. These will help your child to think about what they have read, and to relate the story to their own experiences. The questions are followed by a fun activity.

Enjoy sharing the stories!

Authors and illustrators

Such a Fuss written by Roderick Hunt, illustrated by Nick Schon
The Moon Jet written by Roderick Hunt, illustrated by Nick Schon
Super Dad written by Roderick Hunt, illustrated by Alex Brychta
The Spaceship written by Roderick Hunt, illustrated by Alex Brychta

OXFORD
UNIVERSITY PRESS

Great Clarendon Street, Oxford, OX2 6DP, United Kingdom

Oxford University Press is a department of the University
of Oxford. It furthers the University's objective of excellence
in research, scholarship, and education by publishing
worldwide. Oxford is a registered trade mark of Oxford
University Press in the UK and in certain other countries

The Spaceship, *Super Dad*, *Such a Fuss*, *The Moon Jet*, text © Roderick Hunt
2006, 2007, 2008

Super Dad, *The Spaceship* illustrations © Alex Brychta 2006
Such a Fuss, *The Moon Jet* illustrations © Alex Brychta and Nick Schon 2007

The characters in this work are the original creation of Roderick Hunt
and Alex Brychta who retain copyright in the characters

The moral rights of the author have been asserted

Super Dad, *The Spaceship* first published in 2006
Such a Fuss first published in 2007
The Moon Jet first published in 2008

This Edition first published in 2018

British Library Cataloguing in Publication Data
Data available

ISBN: 978-0-19-276420-1

10 9 8 7 6 5 4 3 2 1

Paper used in the production of this book is a natural, recyclable product
made from wood grown in sustainable forests. The manufacturing process
conforms to the environmental regulations of the country of origin.

Printed in China

Acknowledgements

Series Editors: Annemarie Young and Kate Ruttle

Contents

OXFORD

UNIVERSITY PRESS

Phonics

Children learn best when reading is relaxed and enjoyable.

- Talk about the title and the picture on page 7, and read the speech bubble at the bottom of that page.

- Identify the letter patterns *ch* and *ss* in the title and talk about the sounds they make when you read them.

- Look at the *ch* and *oo* words on page 8. Say the sounds in each word and then say the word (e.g. *s-u-ch*, *such*; *s-oo-n*, *soon*).

- Read the story together, then find the words with *ch*, *oo* and *v* in them.

- Talk about the story and do the fun activity on page 26.

Children enjoy re-reading stories and this helps to build their confidence.

Have fun!

After you have read the story, find the five worms hidden in the pictures.

The main sounds practised in this story are 'ch' as in *Chip*, 'oo' as in *too*, and 'v' as in *Viv*.

For more activities, free eBooks and practical advice to help your child progress with reading visit **oxfordowl.co.uk**

Such a Fuss

Tess makes a big fuss.

Say the sounds and read these words.

Chip	t**oo**
whi**ch**	s**oo**n
mu**ch**	c**oo**l

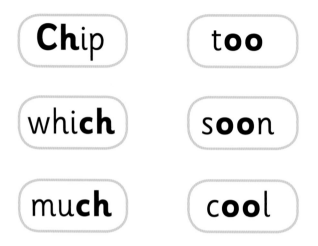

Dad had six hens.

Chip had a hen, too.

"This is Viv," said Chip.

Biff got the eggs.

She put them in a box.

The hens ran up.
Chip fed them.

"Viv is upset," said Chip.
"Such a fuss," said Biff.

Chip put the hens to bed.

But Viv did not go in.

Biff and Chip hid in the shed.

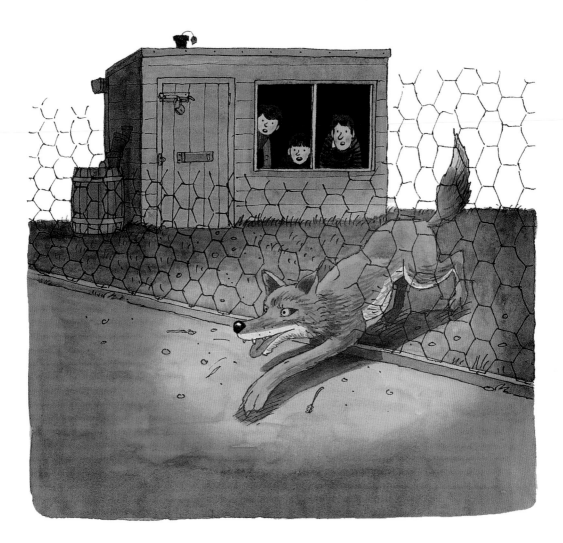

A fox got in.

The fox ran off.

"I can soon fix the pen,"
said Dad.

"Viv is a cool hen," said Chip.

Talk about the story

Who has
six hens?

What is
Chip's hen
called?

Why was
Viv upset?

What kind
of pet would you
like to have?

Missing letters

Choose an ending for the words.

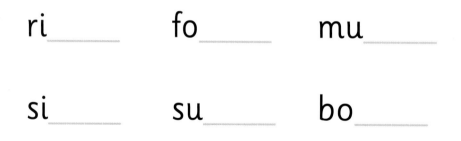

ri _____   fo _____   mu _____

si _____   su _____   bo _____

Tips for reading *The Moon Jet*

Children learn best when reading is relaxed and enjoyable.

● Talk about the title and the picture on page 29, and read the speech bubble at the bottom of that page.

● Identify the letter pattern *oo* in the title and talk about the sound it makes when you read it.

● Look at the *oo* words on page 30. Say the sounds in each word and then say the word (e.g. *m-oo-n*, *moon*).

● Read the story together, then find the words with *oo* in them.

● Talk about the story and do the fun activity on page 48.

Children enjoy re-reading stories and this helps to build their confidence.

Have fun!

After you have read the story, find Little Ted in eight of the pictures.

The main sound practised in this story is 'oo' as in *soon*.

For more activities, free eBooks and practical advice to help your child progress with reading visit **oxfordowl.co.uk**

The Moon Jet

Kipper shoots to the moon!

Say the sounds and read these words.

moon   soon

cool   shoot

zoom   shoo

boom   food

Kipper had a box and a bin.

Kipper got in his jet ...

... and put on the lid.

"This jet is cool," said Kipper.

"Off I go," he said.

The jet shot off.

It shot out of the room.

"I will loop the loop,"
said Kipper.

The jet did six loops.

"I will go to the moon,"
said Kipper.

"I can get to it soon,"
he said.

The jet got to the moon.

But the moon bugs ran up.

"Yuk," said Kipper.
"Moon bugs."

"Shoo, get off," said Kipper.

"Did I nod off?" said Kipper.
"Yes," said Mum. "Get up to bed."

Talk about the story

Where did Kipper go in his jet?

What happened when he got there?

How did Kipper make his jet?

Where would you go if you had a jet?

A maze

Help Kipper to get to the moon.

Stories for Wider Reading

Tips for reading the stories together

These two stories use simple everyday language. You can help your child to read any more challenging words in the context of the story. Children enjoy re-reading stories and this helps to build their confidence and their vocabulary.

Tips for reading *Super Dad*

- Talk about the title and the speech bubble on page 51, and look through the pictures so that your child can see what the story is about.
- Read the story together, encouraging your child to read as much as they can with you.
- Give lots of praise as your child reads with you, and help them when necessary.
- If your child gets stuck on a word that is easily decodable, encourage them to say the sounds and then blend them together to read the word. Read the whole sentence again. Focus on the meaning. If the word is not decodable, or is still too tricky, just read the word for them and move on.
- When you've finished reading the story, talk about it with your child, using the 'Talk about the story' questions at the end.
- Do the activity on page 70.
- Re-read the story later, again encouraging your child to read as much of it as they can.

After you have read *Super Dad*, find a cat hidden in every picture.

Have fun!

This story includes these useful common words:

said   looks   put   stop

For more activities, free eBooks and practical advice to help your child progress with reading visit **oxfordowl.co.uk**

Super Dad

"Look at Dad," said Mum.

"Dad looks silly," said Wilma.

"No, he looks good,"
said Wilf.

Dad put on a red nose.

"Oh no!" said Wilma.
"Dad looks so silly."

Dad had a bucket.

"Put your coins in here,"
he said.

Oh no! A man took
Dad's bucket.

"Stop!" called Mum.
"Come back."

But the man did not stop.

Dad got on a bike.

The man ran fast ...

... but Dad was faster.

"Got you," said Dad.

"Help!" said the man.

"Super Dad!" said Wilma.

Talk about the story

Why did Wilma say that Dad looked silly?

What happened after the man took the bucket?

How did Dad stop the thief?

What would you like to dress up as?

A maze

Help Dad to catch the man.

Tips for reading *The Spaceship*

- Talk about the title and the speech bubble on page 73, and look through the pictures so that your child can see what the story is about.

- Read the story together, encouraging your child to read as much as they can with you.

- Give lots of praise as your child reads with you, and help them when necessary.

- If your child gets stuck on a word that is easily decodable, encourage them to say the sounds and then blend them together to read the word. Read the whole sentence again. Focus on the meaning. If the word is not decodable, or is still too tricky, just read the word for them and move on.

- Read the whole sentence again. Focus on the meaning.

- When you've finished reading the story, talk about it with your child, using the 'Talk about the story' questions at the end.

- Do the activity on page 92.

Have fun!

- Re-read the story later, again encouraging your child to read as much of it as they can.

Find these 10 space bugs hidden in the pictures.

This story includes these useful common words:
said   what   help   them

For more activities, free eBooks and practical advice to help your child progress with reading visit **oxfordowl.co.uk**

The Spaceship

Can Floppy save the spaceship?

Floppy went to sleep and
he began to dream.

A spaceship landed.
"Wow!" said Kipper.
"A real spaceship!"

An alien came out.

"I am Zig," he said.

"And this is my dog, Zog."

"Let's go into space," said Zig.
"Oh yes!" said Kipper.
"Oh no!" said Floppy.

WHOOSH! The spaceship
took off. It flew up into space.

"What's that?" said Kipper.

"Oh no!" shouted Zig.
"Fireballs!"

WHOOSH! Suddenly, there
were fireballs all around them.

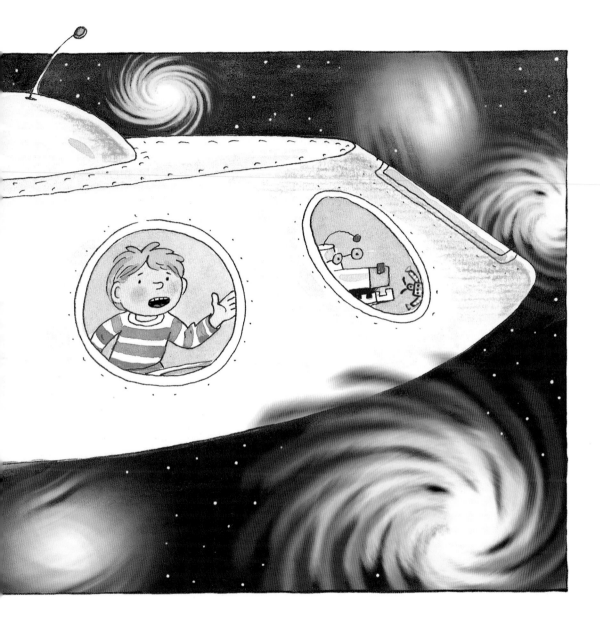

"Help!" shouted Zog.

CRASH! A fireball hit them.
The spaceship began to
spin round.

Zig and Kipper bumped heads.
"Oh, my head!" groaned Kipper.
"Oh, my head!" groaned Zig.

Floppy saw a very big fireball.
It was going to hit them!

"Help!" said Floppy.
"We're in danger!" shouted Zog.
"I don't know what to do."

"I know what to do," said Floppy.
"I can fly the spaceship."

z**OOM!** Floppy flew the
spaceship out of danger.
"Phew! Just in time," he said.

"Well done, Space Dog Floppy,"
said Zig. "You saved us!"

Talk about the story

Why did Floppy dream about space?

How did Floppy feel about being in space?

Why did Floppy have to take control of the spaceship? How did he know what to do?

Where do spaceships go in space? Where would you like to go?

A maze

Help the spaceship find its way through the fireballs to the Earth. Watch out for fireballs!

Remembering the stories together

Encourage your child to remember and retell the stories in this book. You could ask questions like these:

- Who are the characters in the story?
- What happens at the beginning of the story?
- What happens next?
- How does the story end?
- What was your favourite part of the story? Why?

Story prompts

When talking to your child about the stories, you could use these more detailed reminders to help them remember the exact sequence of events. Turn the statements below into questions, so that your child can give you the answers. For example, *What is Chip's hen called? What does Biff collect in a box?* And so on …

Such a Fuss

- Dad has six hens – and Chip has a hen called Viv.
- Biff collects the eggs in a box.
- Chip feeds the hens, but Viv is upset.
- Viv won't go to bed.
- A fox gets into the garden, but Dad scares him off!
- Dad fixes the pen and then Viv is happy again.

The Moon Jet

- Kipper makes a pretend rocket and imagines that he's flying to the moon.
- The jet shoots out of his room.
- The jet does six loops.
- Kipper goes to the moon and meets moon bugs!
- The moon bugs start eating Kipper's rocket.
- Kipper realises he's been dreaming.

94

Super Dad

- Wilf and Wilma's dad dresses up as a superhero.

- Wilma thinks her dad looks silly, but Wilf thinks he looks good.

- Dad puts on a red nose to collect money for charity.

- A man takes Dad's bucket and runs off!

- Dad gets on a bike and chases the man.

- Dad catches the man and Wilma calls him 'Super Dad'!

The Spaceship

- Floppy has a dream that a spaceship has landed.

- Kipper and Floppy meet an alien!

- The alien takes Floppy and Kipper into space.

- There are fireballs all around them.

- Suddenly a fireball hits them and the spaceship begins to spin.

- Floppy flies the spaceship out of danger and saves everyone.

You could now encourage your child to create a 'story map' of each story, drawing and colouring all the key parts of them. This will help them to identify the main elements of the stories and learn to create their own stories.